MY VERY OWN

NATIONAL PARKS JOURNAL

This National Parks jo

_____

OOH LOVELY

How To Use This Journal

For Kids

Every time you visit a National Park, fill in the details in your journal. Write in the name of the park, the state it is in, who you went with and what you saw and did. Give each park a star rating and write or draw your own thoughts about the park. Don't forget to get your park stamp! There are extra sections in this journal for you to doodle and draw some of your favorite scenes and memories from your National Park visit. We hope you have tons of fun visiting, drawing and tracking your time in America's beautiful National Parks with this journal.

For Grownups

This National Park journal is a fun and enjoyable way for you and your child, or family to track your visits. This is an opportunity to develop a beautiful routine together to chat and discuss all you saw and experienced. Young readers can record the sights and activities while getting creative writing or drawing their own reviews of each National Park you tour.

First paperback edition March 2020

Book design by Jennifer Farley
Illustrations Copyright © 2020 by Jennifer Farley

ISBN 978-0-9572837-4-9 (paperback)

Published by ooh lovely.

> "I have a room all to myself.
> It is nature."

– Henry David Thoreau, writer, philosopher

Date I started this journal:

_____

United States Of America
------ National Parks ------

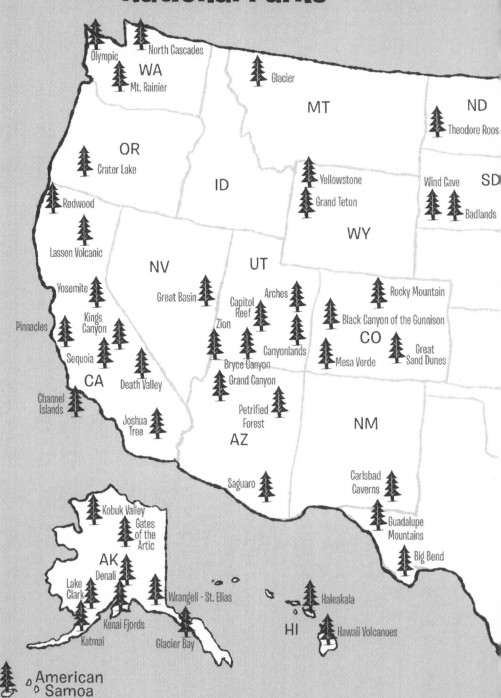

Olympic
North Cascades
WA
Mt. Rainier
Glacier
MT
ND
Theodore Roos
OR
Crater Lake
ID
Yellowstone
Grand Teton
WY
Wind Cave
SD
Badlands
Redwood
Lassen Volcanic
NV
UT
Yosemite
Great Basin
Arches
Capitol Reef
Rocky Mountain
Kings Canyon
Pinnacles
Zion
Black Canyon of the Gunnison
CO
Sequoia
Canyonlands
Mesa Verde
Great Sand Dunes
CA
Death Valley
Bryce Canyon
Grand Canyon
Channel Islands
Joshua Tree
Petrified Forest
NM
AZ
Saguaro
Carlsbad Caverns
Guadalupe Mountains
Big Bend
Kobuk Valley
Gates of the Artic
AK
Denali
Lake Clark
Wrangell - St. Elias
Haleakala
Kenai Fjords
HI
Hawaii Volcanoes
Katmai
Glacier Bay
American Samoa

U.S. National Parks by State

Yellowstone was the first national park, opened in 1872. There are now 61 national parks in twenty nine states and two U.S. territories. The newest national park is White Sands in New Mexico. Here's the full list of parks, by state. Tick them off as you go!

Alaska
Denali National Park
Gates of the Arctic National Park
Glacier Bay National Park
Katmai National Park
Kenai Fjords National Park
Kobuk Valley National Park
Lake Clark National Park
Wrangell-St. Elias National Park

American Samoa
National Park of American Samoa

Arizona
Grand Canyon National Park
Petrified Forest National Park
Saguaro National Park

Arkansas
Hot Springs National Park

California
Channel Islands National Park
Death Valley National Park, CA & Nevada
Joshua Tree National Park
Kings Canyon National Park
Lassen Volcanic National Park
Pinnacles National Park
Redwood National Park
Sequoia National Park
Yosemite National Park

Colorado
Black Canyon of the Gunnison NP
Great Sand Dunes National Park
Mesa Verde National Park
Rocky Mountain National Park

Florida
Biscayne National Park
Dry Tortugas National Park
Everglades National Park

Hawaii
Haleakala National Park
Hawai'i Volcanoes National Park

Idaho
Yellowstone National Park, Idaho, Montana, and Wyoming

Kentucky
Mammoth Cave National Park

Illinois
Gateway Arch NP, IL and Missouri

Indiana
Indiana Dunes National Park

Maine
Acadia National Park, Maine

Michigan
Isle Royale National Park

Minnesota
Voyageurs National Park

Missouri
Gateway Arch NP, MO and IL

Montana
Glacier National Park
Yellowstone National Park, Idaho,
Montana, and Wyoming

Nevada
Death Valley National Park
Great Basin National Park

New Mexico
Carlsbad Caverns National Park

North Dakota
Theodore Roosevelt NP

North Carolina
Great Smoky Mountains NP,
North Carolina and Tennessee

Ohio
Cuyahoga Valley National Park

Oregon
Crater Lake National Park

South Carolina
Congaree National Park

South Dakota
Badlands National Park
Wind Cave National Park

Tennessee
Great Smoky Mountains NP
North Carolina and Tennessee

Texas
Big Bend National Park
Guadalupe Mountains NP

Utah
Arches National Park
Bryce Canyon National Park
Canyonlands National Park
Capitol Reef National Park
Zion National Park

Virgin Islands
Virgin Islands National Park

Virginia
Shenandoah National Park

Washington
Mount Rainier National Park
North Cascades National Park
Olympic National Park

Wyoming
Grand Teton National Park
Yellowstone National Park
Idaho, Montana, and Wyoming

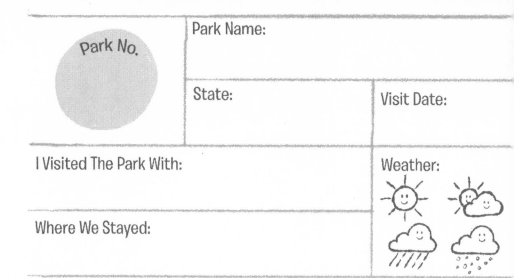

Park No.

Park Name:

State:

Visit Date:

I Visited The Park With:

Where We Stayed:

Weather:

Sights I Saw:

Wildlife I Saw:

Park stamp and my notes about the park (write or draw!)

Would I Like To Visit Again ?   Yes ☐   No ☐

Star rating (color in)   ☆ ☆ ☆ ☆ ☆

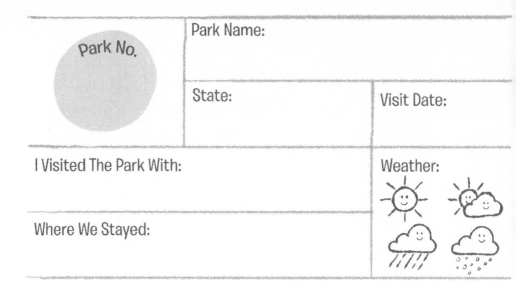

Park No.

Park Name:

State:

Visit Date:

I Visited The Park With:

Where We Stayed:

Weather:

Sights I Saw:

Wildlife I Saw:

Park stamp and my notes about the park (write or draw!)

Would I Like To Visit Again ?   Yes ☐   No ☐

Star rating (color in)   ☆ ☆ ☆ ☆ ☆

Park No.

Park Name:

State:

Visit Date:

I Visited The Park With:

Where We Stayed:

Weather:

Sights I Saw:

Wildlife I Saw:

Park stamp and my notes about the park (write or draw!)

Would I Like To Visit Again ?   Yes ☐   No ☐

Star rating (color in) ☆ ☆ ☆ ☆ ☆

Park No.

Park Name:

State:

Visit Date:

I Visited The Park With:

Weather:

Where We Stayed:

Sights I Saw:

Wildlife I Saw:

Park stamp and my notes about the park (write or draw!)

Would I Like To Visit Again ?   Yes ☐   No ☐

Star rating (color in) ☆ ☆ ☆ ☆ ☆

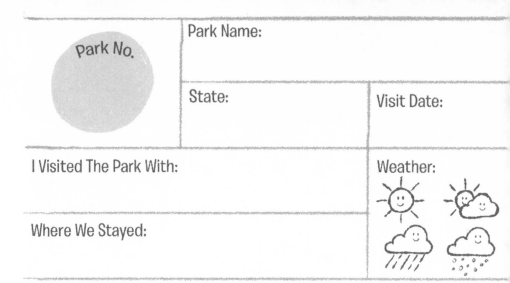

Park No.

Park Name:

State:

Visit Date:

I Visited The Park With:

Where We Stayed:

Weather:

Sights I Saw:

Wildlife I Saw:

Park stamp and my notes about the park (write or draw!)

Would I Like To Visit Again ?   Yes ☐   No ☐

Star rating (color in)   ☆ ☆ ☆ ☆ ☆

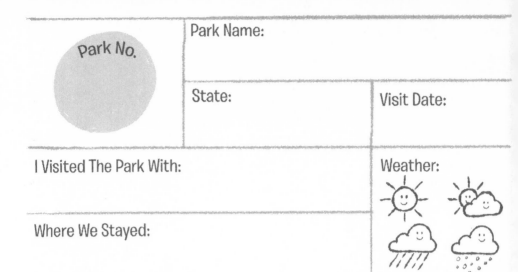

Park No.

Park Name:

State:

Visit Date:

I Visited The Park With:

Where We Stayed:

Weather:

Sights I Saw:

Wildlife I Saw:

Park stamp and my notes about the park (write or draw!)

Would I Like To Visit Again ?   Yes ☐   No ☐

Star rating (color in)   ☆ ☆ ☆ ☆ ☆

Park No.

Park Name:

State:

Visit Date:

I Visited The Park With:

Where We Stayed:

Weather:

Sights I Saw:

Wildlife I Saw:

Park stamp and my notes about the park (write or draw!)

Would I Like To Visit Again ?   Yes ☐   No ☐

Star rating (color in)   ☆ ☆ ☆ ☆ ☆

Park No.

Park Name:

State:

Visit Date:

I Visited The Park With:

Where We Stayed:

Weather:

Sights I Saw:

Wildlife I Saw:

Park stamp and my notes about the park (write or draw!)

Would I Like To Visit Again ?   Yes ☐   No ☐

Star rating (color in)   ☆ ☆ ☆ ☆ ☆

Draw some of the favorite things you've seen.

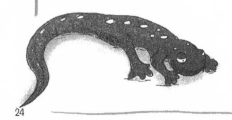

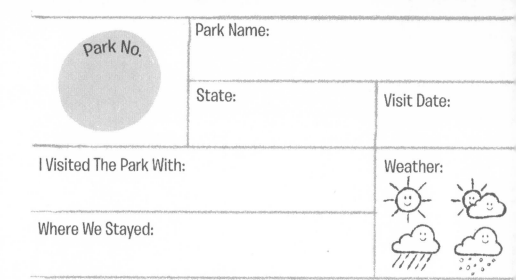

Park No.

Park Name:

State:

Visit Date:

I Visited The Park With:

Where We Stayed:

Weather:

Sights I Saw:

Wildlife I Saw:

Park stamp and my notes about the park (write or draw!)

Would I Like To Visit Again ?   Yes ☐   No ☐

Star rating (color in)   ☆ ☆ ☆ ☆ ☆

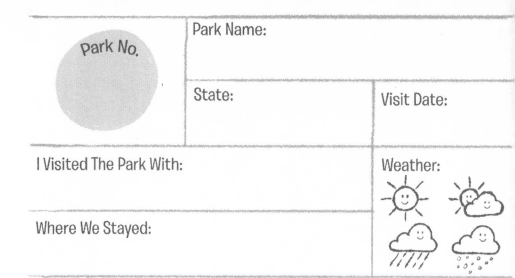

Park No.

Park Name:

State:

Visit Date:

I Visited The Park With:

Where We Stayed:

Weather:

Sights I Saw:

Wildlife I Saw:

Park stamp and my notes about the park (write or draw!)

Would I Like To Visit Again ?   Yes ☐   No ☐

Star rating (color in)   ☆ ☆ ☆ ☆ ☆

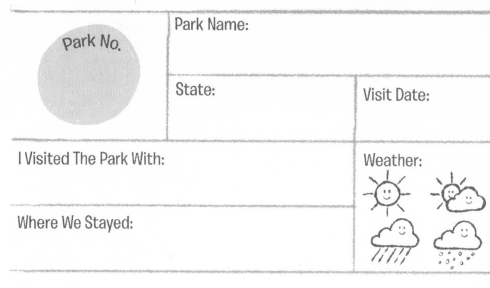

Park No.

Park Name:

State:

Visit Date:

I Visited The Park With:

Where We Stayed:

Weather:

Sights I Saw:

Wildlife I Saw:

Park stamp and my notes about the park (write or draw!)

Would I Like To Visit Again ?   Yes ☐   No ☐

Star rating (color in)   ☆ ☆ ☆ ☆ ☆

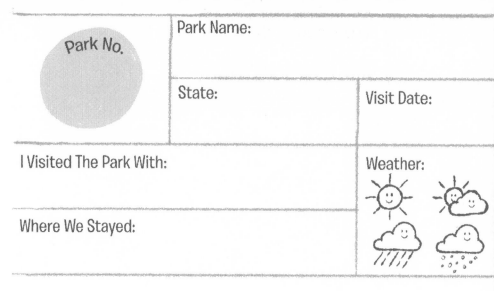

Park No.

Park Name:

State:

Visit Date:

I Visited The Park With:

Where We Stayed:

Weather:

Sights I Saw:

Wildlife I Saw:

Park stamp and my notes about the park (write or draw!)

Would I Like To Visit Again ?   Yes ☐   No ☐

Star rating (color in)   ☆ ☆ ☆ ☆ ☆

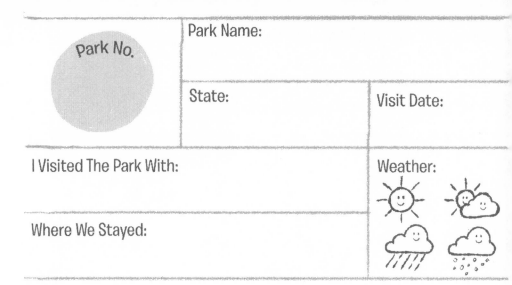

Park No.

Park Name:

State:

Visit Date:

I Visited The Park With:

Where We Stayed:

Weather:

Sights I Saw:

Wildlife I Saw:

Park stamp and my notes about the park (write or draw!)

Would I Like To Visit Again ?   Yes ☐   No ☐

Star rating (color in)   ☆ ☆ ☆ ☆ ☆

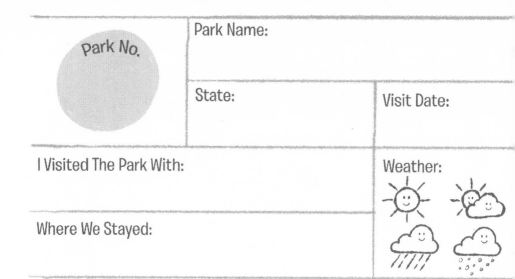

Park No.

Park Name:

State:

Visit Date:

I Visited The Park With:

Where We Stayed:

Weather:

Sights I Saw:

Wildlife I Saw:

Park stamp and my notes about the park (write or draw!)

Would I Like To Visit Again ?   Yes ☐   No ☐

Star rating (color in)

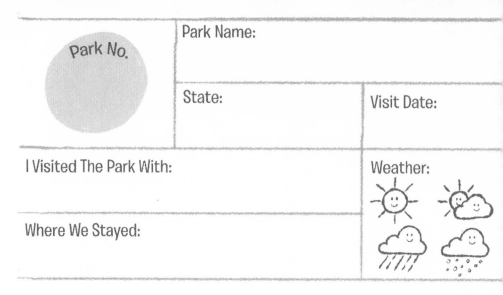

Park No.

Park Name:

State:

Visit Date:

I Visited The Park With:

Where We Stayed:

Weather:

Sights I Saw:

Wildlife I Saw:

Park stamp and my notes about the park (write or draw!)

Would I Like To Visit Again ?   Yes ☐   No ☐

Star rating (color in) ☆ ☆ ☆ ☆ ☆

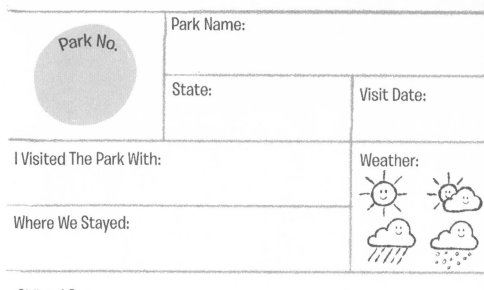

Park No.

Park Name:

State:

Visit Date:

I Visited The Park With:

Where We Stayed:

Weather:

Sights I Saw:

Wildlife I Saw:

Park stamp and my notes about the park (write or draw!)

Would I Like To Visit Again ?   Yes ☐   No ☐

Star rating (color in) ☆ ☆ ☆ ☆ ☆

Draw some of the favorite things you've seen.

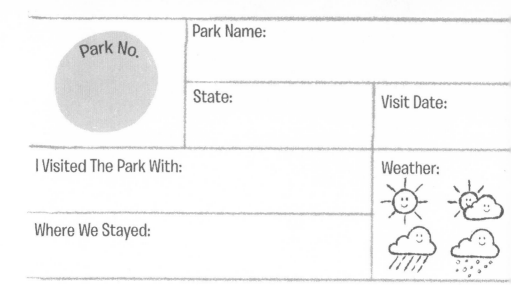

Park No.

Park Name:

State:

Visit Date:

I Visited The Park With:

Where We Stayed:

Weather:

Sights I Saw:

Wildlife I Saw:

Park stamp and my notes about the park (write or draw!)

Would I Like To Visit Again ?   Yes ☐   No ☐

Star rating (color in) ☆ ☆ ☆ ☆ ☆

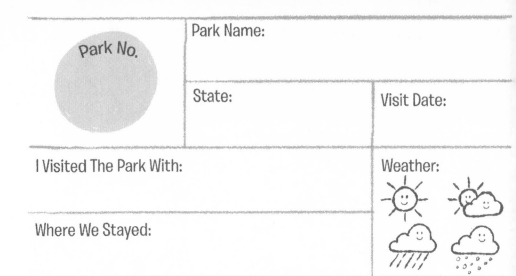

Park No.

Park Name:

State:

Visit Date:

I Visited The Park With:

Where We Stayed:

Weather:

Sights I Saw:

Wildlife I Saw:

Park stamp and my notes about the park (write or draw!)

Would I Like To Visit Again ?   Yes ☐   No ☐

Star rating (color in)   ☆ ☆ ☆ ☆ ☆

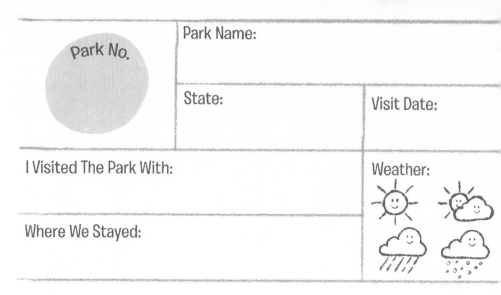

Park No.

Park Name:

State:

Visit Date:

I Visited The Park With:

Where We Stayed:

Weather:

Sights I Saw:

Wildlife I Saw:

Park stamp and my notes about the park (write or draw!)

Would I Like To Visit Again ?   Yes ☐   No ☐

Star rating (color in)   ☆ ☆ ☆ ☆ ☆

Park No.

Park Name:

State:

Visit Date:

I Visited The Park With:

Where We Stayed:

Weather:

Sights I Saw:

Wildlife I Saw:

Park stamp and my notes about the park (write or draw!)

Would I Like To Visit Again ?   Yes ☐   No ☐

Star rating (color in) ☆ ☆ ☆ ☆ ☆

Park No.

Park Name:

State:

Visit Date:

I Visited The Park With:

Where We Stayed:

Weather:

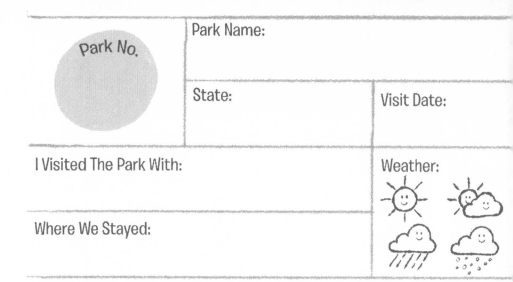

Sights I Saw:

Wildlife I Saw:

Park stamp and my notes about the park (write or draw!)

Would I Like To Visit Again ?   Yes ☐   No ☐

Star rating (color in)   ☆ ☆ ☆ ☆ ☆

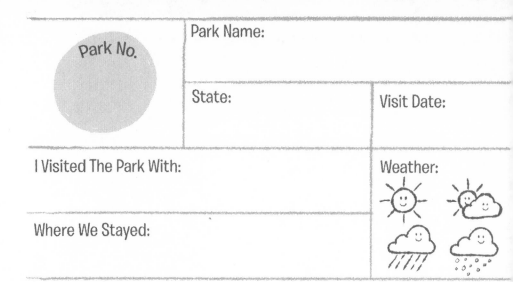

Park No.

Park Name:

State:

Visit Date:

I Visited The Park With:

Where We Stayed:

Weather:

Sights I Saw:

Wildlife I Saw:

Park stamp and my notes about the park (write or draw!)

Would I Like To Visit Again ?   Yes ☐   No ☐

Star rating (color in) ☆ ☆ ☆ ☆ ☆

Park No.

Park Name:

State:

Visit Date:

I Visited The Park With:

Where We Stayed:

Weather:

Sights I Saw:

Wildlife I Saw:

Park stamp and my notes about the park (write or draw!)

Would I Like To Visit Again ?   Yes ☐   No ☐

Star rating (color in)   ☆ ☆ ☆ ☆ ☆

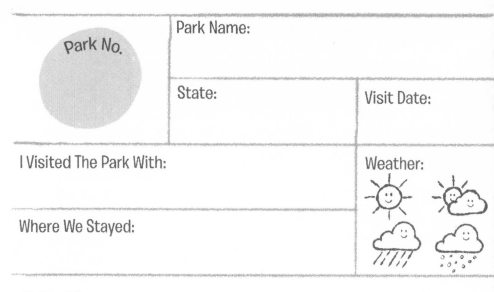

Park No.

Park Name:

State:

Visit Date:

I Visited The Park With:

Where We Stayed:

Weather:

Sights I Saw:

Wildlife I Saw:

Park stamp and my notes about the park (write or draw!)

Would I Like To Visit Again ?   Yes ☐   No ☐

Star rating (color in) ☆ ☆ ☆ ☆ ☆

Draw some of the favorite things you've seen.

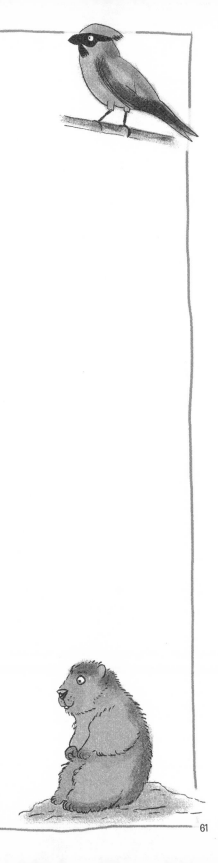

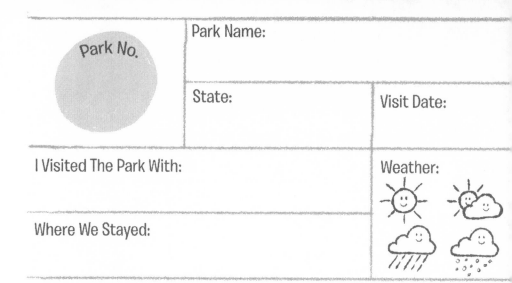

Park No.

Park Name:

State:

Visit Date:

I Visited The Park With:

Where We Stayed:

Weather:

Sights I Saw:

Wildlife I Saw:

Park stamp and my notes about the park (write or draw!)

Would I Like To Visit Again ?   Yes ☐   No ☐

Star rating (color in) ☆ ☆ ☆ ☆ ☆

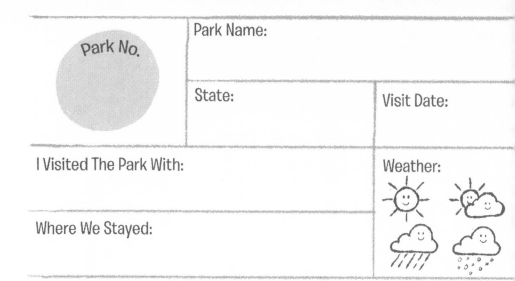

Park No.

Park Name:

State:

Visit Date:

I Visited The Park With:

Where We Stayed:

Weather:

Sights I Saw:

Wildlife I Saw:

Park stamp and my notes about the park (write or draw!)

Would I Like To Visit Again ?   Yes ☐   No ☐

Star rating (color in)

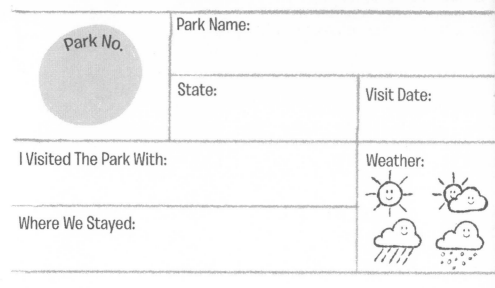

Park No.

Park Name:

State:

Visit Date:

I Visited The Park With:

Where We Stayed:

Weather:

Sights I Saw:

Wildlife I Saw:

Park stamp and my notes about the park (write or draw!)

Would I Like To Visit Again ?   Yes ☐   No ☐

Star rating (color in) ☆ ☆ ☆ ☆ ☆

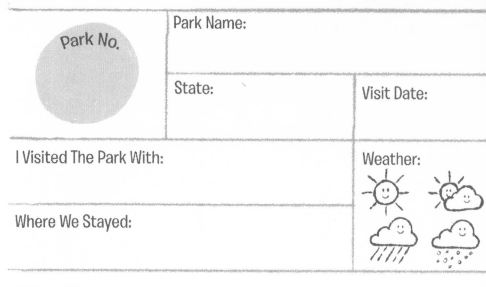

Park No.

Park Name:

State:

Visit Date:

I Visited The Park With:

Where We Stayed:

Weather:

Sights I Saw:

Wildlife I Saw:

Park stamp and my notes about the park (write or draw!)

Would I Like To Visit Again ?   Yes ☐   No ☐

Star rating (color in) ☆ ☆ ☆ ☆ ☆

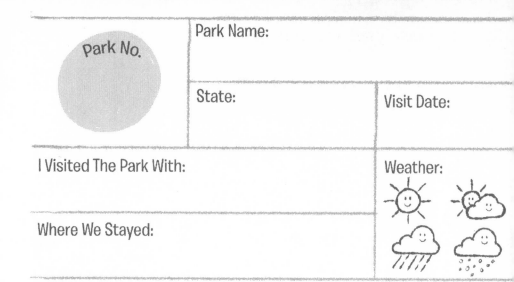

Park No.

Park Name:

State:

Visit Date:

I Visited The Park With:

Where We Stayed:

Weather:

Sights I Saw:

Wildlife I Saw:

Park stamp and my notes about the park (write or draw!)

Would I Like To Visit Again ?   Yes ☐   No ☐

Star rating (color in)   ☆ ☆ ☆ ☆ ☆

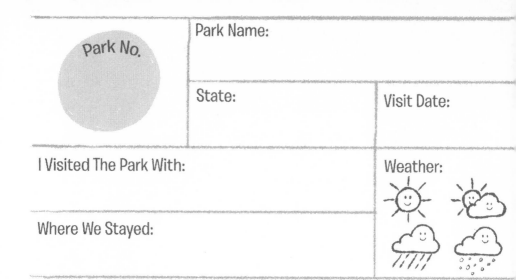

Park No.

Park Name:

State:

Visit Date:

I Visited The Park With:

Where We Stayed:

Weather:

Sights I Saw:

Wildlife I Saw:

Park stamp and my notes about the park (write or draw!)

Would I Like To Visit Again ?   Yes ☐   No ☐

Star rating (color in)   ☆ ☆ ☆ ☆ ☆

Park No.

Park Name:

State:

Visit Date:

I Visited The Park With:

Where We Stayed:

Weather:

Sights I Saw:

Wildlife I Saw:

Park stamp and my notes about the park (write or draw!)

Would I Like To Visit Again ?   Yes ☐   No ☐

Star rating (color in)   ☆ ☆ ☆ ☆ ☆

Park No.

Park Name:

State:

Visit Date:

I Visited The Park With:

Where We Stayed:

Weather:

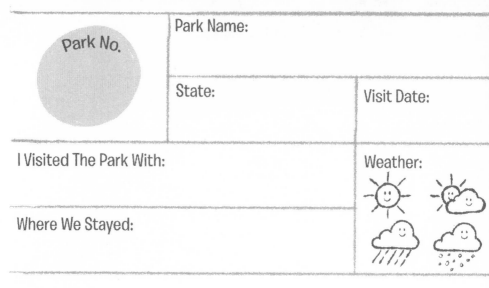

Sights I Saw:

Wildlife I Saw:

Park stamp and my notes about the park (write or draw!)

Would I Like To Visit Again ?   Yes ☐   No ☐

Star rating (color in) ☆ ☆ ☆ ☆ ☆

Draw some of the favorite things you've seen.

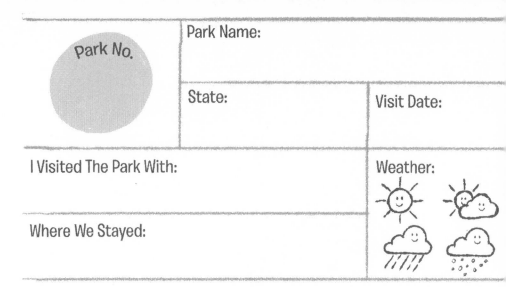

Park No.

Park Name:

State:

Visit Date:

I Visited The Park With:

Where We Stayed:

Weather:

Sights I Saw:

Wildlife I Saw:

Park stamp and my notes about the park (write or draw!)

Would I Like To Visit Again ?   Yes ☐   No ☐

Star rating (color in)   ☆ ☆ ☆ ☆ ☆

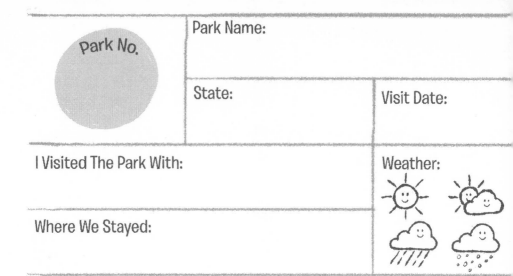

	Park Name:	
Park No.	State:	Visit Date:

I Visited The Park With:	Weather:
Where We Stayed:	

Sights I Saw:

Wildlife I Saw:

Park stamp and my notes about the park (write or draw!)

Would I Like To Visit Again ?   Yes ☐   No ☐

Star rating (color in) ☆ ☆ ☆ ☆ ☆

Park No.

Park Name:

State:

Visit Date:

I Visited The Park With:

Where We Stayed:

Weather:

Sights I Saw:

Wildlife I Saw:

Park stamp and my notes about the park (write or draw!)

Would I Like To Visit Again ?   Yes ☐   No ☐

Star rating (color in) ☆ ☆ ☆ ☆ ☆

Park No.

Park Name:

State:

Visit Date:

I Visited The Park With:

Where We Stayed:

Weather:

Sights I Saw:

Wildlife I Saw:

Park stamp and my notes about the park (write or draw!)

Would I Like To Visit Again ?   Yes ☐   No ☐

Star rating (color in)   ☆ ☆ ☆ ☆ ☆

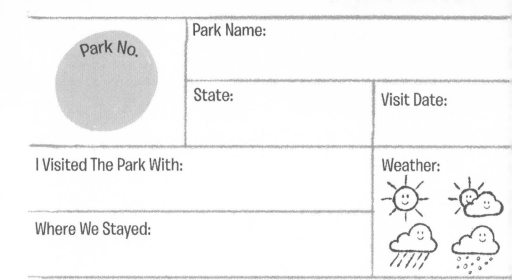

Park No.

Park Name:

State:

Visit Date:

I Visited The Park With:

Where We Stayed:

Weather:

Sights I Saw:

Wildlife I Saw:

Park stamp and my notes about the park (write or draw!)

Would I Like To Visit Again ?   Yes ☐   No ☐

Star rating (color in)   ☆ ☆ ☆ ☆ ☆

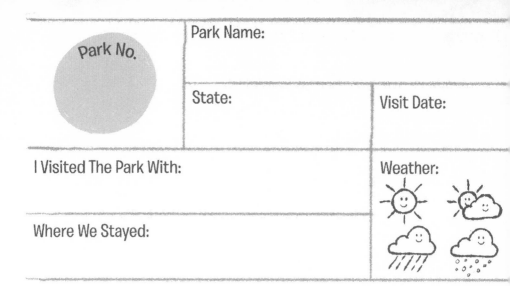

Park No.

Park Name:

State:

Visit Date:

I Visited The Park With:

Where We Stayed:

Weather:

Sights I Saw:

Wildlife I Saw:

Park stamp and my notes about the park (write or draw!)

Would I Like To Visit Again ?   Yes ☐   No ☐

Star rating (color in)

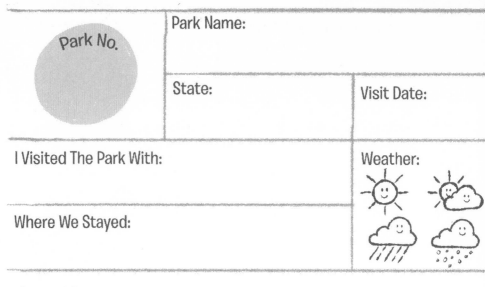

Park No.

Park Name:

State:

Visit Date:

I Visited The Park With:

Where We Stayed:

Weather:

Sights I Saw:

Wildlife I Saw:

Park stamp and my notes about the park (write or draw!)

Would I Like To Visit Again ?   Yes ☐   No ☐

Star rating (color in) ☆ ☆ ☆ ☆ ☆

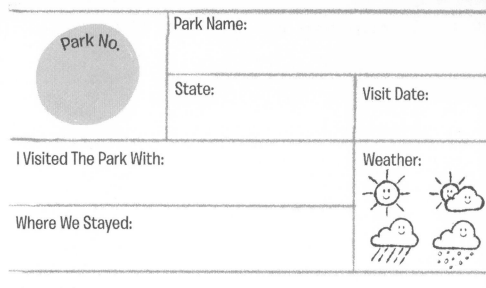

Park No.

Park Name:

State:

Visit Date:

I Visited The Park With:

Where We Stayed:

Weather:

Sights I Saw:

Wildlife I Saw:

Park stamp and my notes about the park (write or draw!)

Would I Like To Visit Again ?   Yes ☐   No ☐

Star rating (color in) ☆ ☆ ☆ ☆ ☆

Draw some of the favorite things you've seen.

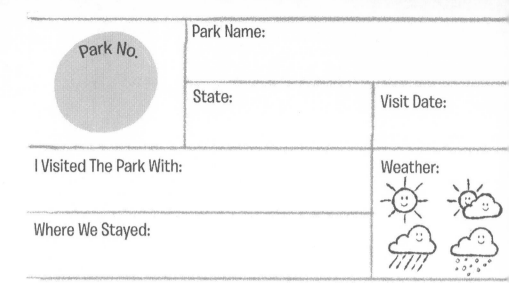

Park No.

Park Name:

State:

Visit Date:

I Visited The Park With:

Where We Stayed:

Weather:

Sights I Saw:

Wildlife I Saw:

Park stamp and my notes about the park (write or draw!)

Would I Like To Visit Again ?   Yes ☐   No ☐

Star rating (color in)   ☆ ☆ ☆ ☆ ☆

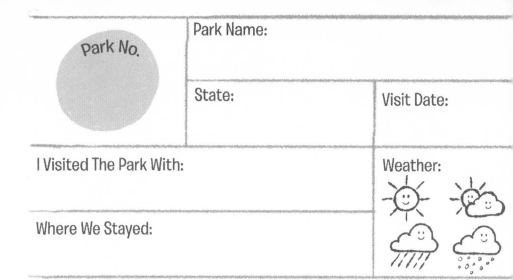

Park No.

Park Name:

State:

Visit Date:

I Visited The Park With:

Where We Stayed:

Weather:

Sights I Saw:

Wildlife I Saw:

Park stamp and my notes about the park (write or draw!)

Would I Like To Visit Again ?   Yes ☐   No ☐

Star rating (color in) ☆ ☆ ☆ ☆ ☆

Park No.

Park Name:

State:

Visit Date:

I Visited The Park With:

Where We Stayed:

Weather:

Sights I Saw:

Wildlife I Saw:

Park stamp and my notes about the park (write or draw!)

Would I Like To Visit Again ?   Yes ☐   No ☐

Star rating (color in)   ☆ ☆ ☆ ☆ ☆

Park No.

Park Name:

State:

Visit Date:

I Visited The Park With:

Where We Stayed:

Weather:

Sights I Saw:

Wildlife I Saw:

Park stamp and my notes about the park (write or draw!)

Would I Like To Visit Again ?   Yes ☐   No ☐

Star rating (color in)   ☆ ☆ ☆ ☆ ☆

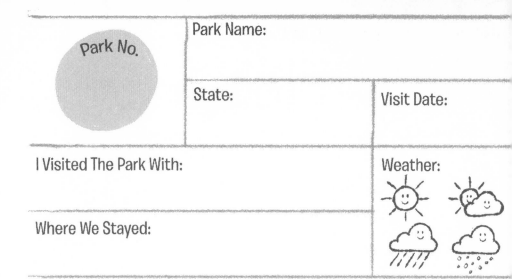

Park No.

Park Name:

State:

Visit Date:

I Visited The Park With:

Where We Stayed:

Weather:

Sights I Saw:

Wildlife I Saw:

Park stamp and my notes about the park (write or draw!)

Would I Like To Visit Again ?   Yes ☐   No ☐

Star rating (color in) ☆ ☆ ☆ ☆ ☆

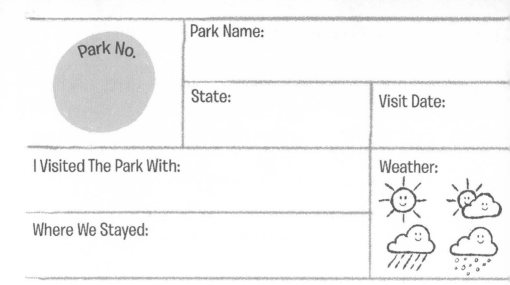

Park No.

Park Name:

State:

Visit Date:

I Visited The Park With:

Where We Stayed:

Weather:

Sights I Saw:

Wildlife I Saw:

Park stamp and my notes about the park (write or draw!)

Would I Like To Visit Again ?   Yes ☐   No ☐

Star rating (color in)   ☆ ☆ ☆ ☆ ☆

Park No.

Park Name:

State:

Visit Date:

I Visited The Park With:

Where We Stayed:

Weather:

Sights I Saw:

Wildlife I Saw:

Park stamp and my notes about the park (write or draw!)

Would I Like To Visit Again ?　　　Yes ☐　　　No ☐

Star rating (color in)　☆ ☆ ☆ ☆ ☆

Park No.

Park Name:

State:

Visit Date:

I Visited The Park With:

Where We Stayed:

Weather:

Sights I Saw:

Wildlife I Saw:

Park stamp and my notes about the park (write or draw!)

Would I Like To Visit Again ?   Yes ☐   No ☐

Star rating (color in)   ☆ ☆ ☆ ☆ ☆

Draw some of the favorite things you've seen.

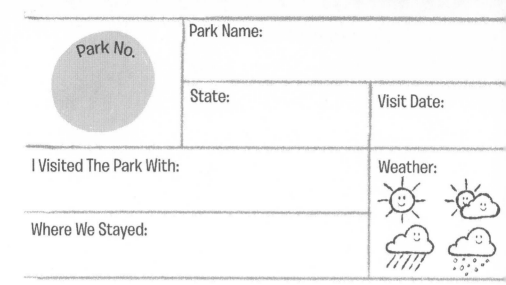

Park No.

Park Name:

State:

Visit Date:

I Visited The Park With:

Where We Stayed:

Weather:

Sights I Saw:

Wildlife I Saw:

Park stamp and my notes about the park (write or draw!)

Would I Like To Visit Again ?   Yes ☐   No ☐

Star rating (color in) ☆ ☆ ☆ ☆ ☆

Park No.

Park Name:

State:

Visit Date:

I Visited The Park With:

Weather:

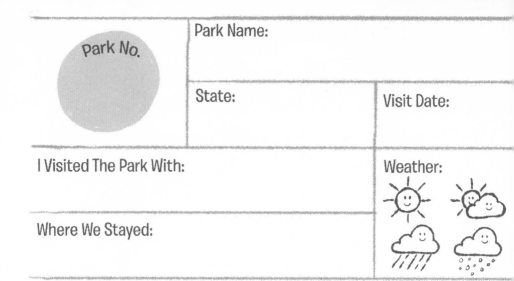

Where We Stayed:

Sights I Saw:

Wildlife I Saw:

Park stamp and my notes about the park (write or draw!)

Would I Like To Visit Again ?   Yes ☐   No ☐

Star rating (color in)   ☆ ☆ ☆ ☆ ☆

Park No.

Park Name:

State:

Visit Date:

I Visited The Park With:

Where We Stayed:

Weather:

Sights I Saw:

Wildlife I Saw:

Park stamp and my notes about the park (write or draw!)

Would I Like To Visit Again ?   Yes ☐   No ☐

Star rating (color in)   ☆ ☆ ☆ ☆ ☆

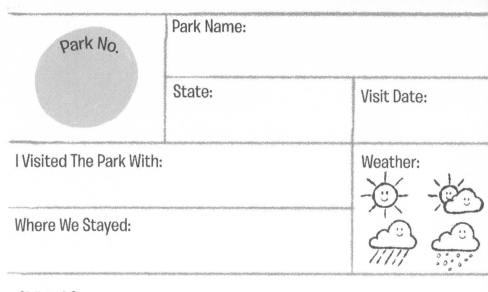

Park No.

Park Name:

State:

Visit Date:

I Visited The Park With:

Where We Stayed:

Weather:

Sights I Saw:

Wildlife I Saw:

Park stamp and my notes about the park (write or draw!)

Would I Like To Visit Again ?   Yes ☐   No ☐

Star rating (color in)   ☆ ☆ ☆ ☆ ☆

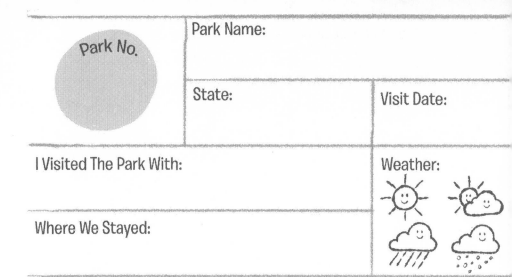

Park No.

Park Name:

State:

Visit Date:

I Visited The Park With:

Where We Stayed:

Weather:

Sights I Saw:

Wildlife I Saw:

Park stamp and my notes about the park (write or draw!)

Would I Like To Visit Again ?   Yes ☐   No ☐

Star rating (color in) ☆ ☆ ☆ ☆ ☆

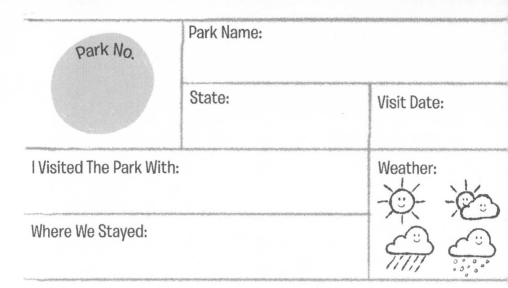

Park No.

Park Name:

State:

Visit Date:

I Visited The Park With:

Where We Stayed:

Weather:

Sights I Saw:

Wildlife I Saw:

Park stamp and my notes about the park (write or draw!)

Would I Like To Visit Again ?   Yes ☐   No ☐

Star rating (color in) ☆ ☆ ☆ ☆ ☆

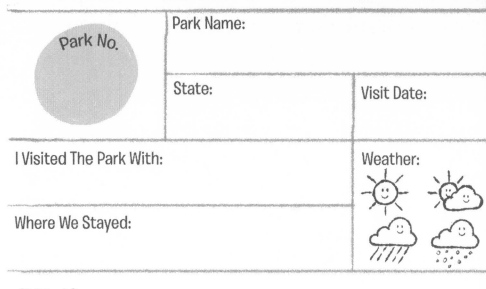

Park No.

Park Name:

State:

Visit Date:

I Visited The Park With:

Where We Stayed:

Weather:

Sights I Saw:

Wildlife I Saw:

Park stamp and my notes about the park (write or draw!)

Would I Like To Visit Again ?   Yes ☐   No ☐

Star rating (color in) ☆ ☆ ☆ ☆ ☆

Park No.

Park Name:

State:

Visit Date:

I Visited The Park With:

Where We Stayed:

Weather:

Sights I Saw:

Wildlife I Saw:

Park stamp and my notes about the park (write or draw!)

Would I Like To Visit Again ?   Yes ☐   No ☐

Star rating (color in)   ☆ ☆ ☆ ☆ ☆

Draw some of the favorite things you've seen.

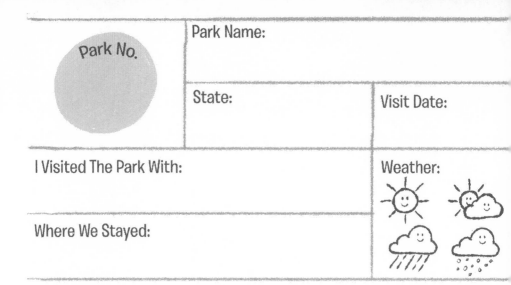

Park No.

Park Name:

State:

Visit Date:

I Visited The Park With:

Where We Stayed:

Weather:

Sights I Saw:

Wildlife I Saw:

Park stamp and my notes about the park (write or draw!)

Would I Like To Visit Again ?   Yes ☐   No ☐

Star rating (color in)   ☆ ☆ ☆ ☆ ☆

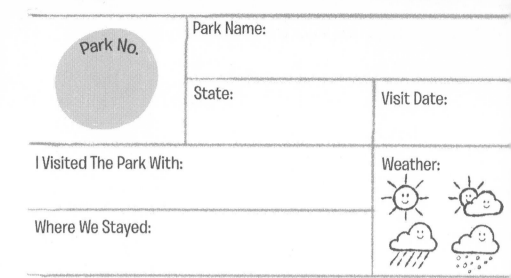

Park No.

Park Name:

State:

Visit Date:

I Visited The Park With:

Where We Stayed:

Weather:

Sights I Saw:

Wildlife I Saw:

Park stamp and my notes about the park (write or draw!)

Would I Like To Visit Again ?   Yes ☐   No ☐

Star rating (color in) ☆ ☆ ☆ ☆ ☆

Park No.

Park Name:

State:

Visit Date:

I Visited The Park With:

Where We Stayed:

Weather:

Sights I Saw:

Wildlife I Saw:

Park stamp and my notes about the park (write or draw!)

Would I Like To Visit Again ?   Yes ☐   No ☐

Star rating (color in)   ☆ ☆ ☆ ☆ ☆

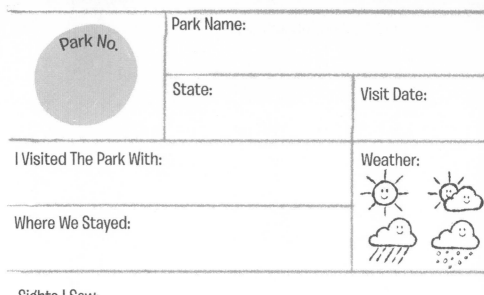

Park No.

Park Name:

State:

Visit Date:

I Visited The Park With:

Where We Stayed:

Weather:

Sights I Saw:

Wildlife I Saw:

Park stamp and my notes about the park (write or draw!)

Would I Like To Visit Again ?   Yes ☐   No ☐

Star rating (color in) ☆ ☆ ☆ ☆ ☆

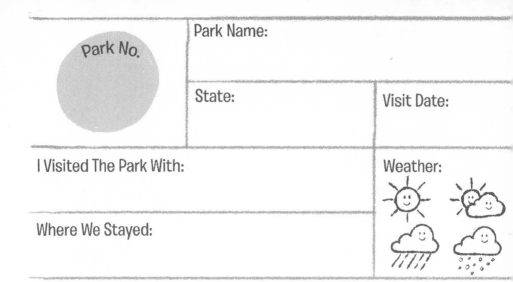

Park No.

Park Name:

State:

Visit Date:

I Visited The Park With:

Where We Stayed:

Weather:

Sights I Saw:

Wildlife I Saw:

Park stamp and my notes about the park (write or draw!)

Would I Like To Visit Again ?   Yes ☐   No ☐

Star rating (color in) ☆ ☆ ☆ ☆ ☆

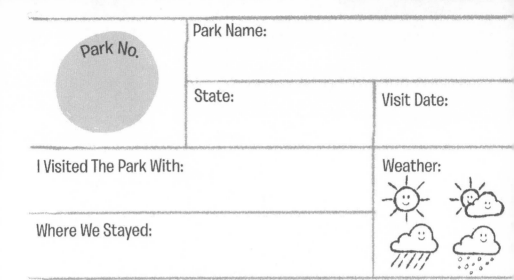

Park No.

Park Name:

State:

Visit Date:

I Visited The Park With:

Where We Stayed:

Weather:

Sights I Saw:

Wildlife I Saw:

Park stamp and my notes about the park (write or draw!)

Would I Like To Visit Again ?   Yes ☐   No ☐

Star rating (color in)

Park No.

Park Name:

State:

Visit Date:

I Visited The Park With:

Weather:

Where We Stayed:

Sights I Saw:

Wildlife I Saw:

Park stamp and my notes about the park (write or draw!)

Would I Like To Visit Again ?   Yes ☐   No ☐

Star rating (color in)   ☆ ☆ ☆ ☆ ☆

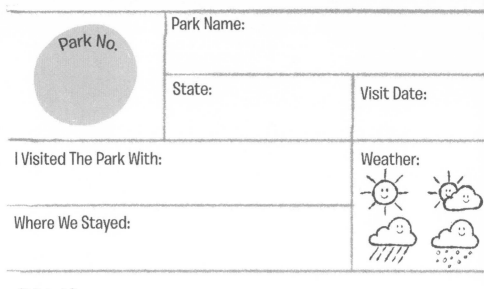

Park No.

Park Name:

State:

Visit Date:

I Visited The Park With:

Where We Stayed:

Weather:

Sights I Saw:

Wildlife I Saw:

Park stamp and my notes about the park (write or draw!)

Would I Like To Visit Again ?   Yes ☐   No ☐

Star rating (color in)   ☆ ☆ ☆ ☆ ☆

Draw some of the favorite things you've seen.

"Take nothing but pictures.
Leave nothing but footprints.
Kill nothing but time."

Date I completed this journal:

_____

Made in the USA
Monee, IL
26 May 2022